Diaphenia
Damelus' song to his Diaphenia

Corydon, arise!

Phyllida's love-call to her Corydon, and his replying

Shall we go dance?

When Mary thro' the garden went

When Ma-ry thro' the gar-den went, the dew lay still _____ on flower and grass, _____

When Ma-ry thro' the gar - den went, the dew lay still _____ on flower and

When Ma-ry thro' the gar - den went, the dew lay still _____ on flower and

When Ma-ry thro' the gar - den went, the dew lay still _____ on flower and

_____ The wav - ing palms a - bove her sent their fra - grance out as ___

grass, The wav - ing palms a - bove her ___ sent their fra - grance out ___ as ___

grass, The wav - ing palms a - bove her sent their fra - grance out as

grass, The wav - ing palms ___ a - bove her sent their fra - grance out as

she did pass. No light up-on their branch-es was. When

she did ___ pass. No light up-on their branch-es was. When

she did pass. ___ No light up-on their branch-es was. When

she did ___ pass. No light up-on their branch-es was. When

The blue bird

* Or one or a few voices, the remaining sopranos taking Alto 1 part

24

The haven

* T1: a, T2: b

Chillingham

Choral Programme Series

Choral repertoire builders with a difference!

Each volume in this brand-new series offers 20–30 minutes of choral music, designed to assist all SATB choirs, large and small, amateur and professional, in imaginative concert programming. Repertoire is drawn from the 18th, 19th and 20th centuries, as well as new commissions, with the emphasis on unavailable, unpublished or unknown material. With expert guidance from Consultant Editor Simon Halsey, maximum practicality is ensured, making the *Choral Programme Series* an invaluable addition to SATB concert repertoire.

Imaginative, versatile and great value for money!

The Choral Programme Series:

Gilbert & Sullivan – Opera Choruses 1
SATB/keyboard. Edited by Ronald Corp

Eagle high in cloudland soaring (*Utopia Limited*)
Strange adventure (*The Yeomen of the Guard*)
Brightly dawns our wedding day (*The Mikado*)
Tho' p'raps I may incur your blame (*Iolanthe*)
I rejoice that it's decided (*The Sorcerer*)
I hear the soft note (*Patience*)

Gilbert & Sullivan – Opera Choruses 2
SATB/keyboard. Edited by Ronald Corp

When the buds are blossoming (*Ruddigore*)
The world is but a broken toy (*Princess Ida*)
Try we life-long (*The Gondoliers*)
Strange the views some people hold
(*The Grand Duke*)
A nice dilemma (*Trial by Jury*)
Hail Poetry (*The Pirates of Penzance*)

Franz Schubert – Four Partsongs
SATB/keyboard. Edited by Judith Blezzard

Lebenslust
An die Sonne
Schicksalslenker
Der Tanz

C.V. Stanford – Seven Partsongs
SATB

Diaphenia
Corydon, arise!
Shall we go dance?
When Mary thro' the garden went
The blue bird
The haven
Chillingham

Five English Folksongs
SATB. Arranged by Daryl Runswick

Dance to thy daddy
She moved through the fair
The frog and the crow
Scarborough Fair
Bobby Shaftoe

Five American Folksongs
SATB. Arranged by Daryl Runswick

Yankee Doodle
Shenandoah
Shortnin' bread – Pick a bale o' cotton
The streets of Laredo
Frog went a-courtin'

Faber Music 3 Queen Square London WC1N 3AU

ISBN 0-571-51272-0

9 780571 512720